Bzzz ... Splat!
The Impact Poetry Book

Selected by Catherine Baker

Contents

SPOTS

They arrive in the night
With beams on their faces
And zit themselves down
In hard to find places.

The end of my nose
Is a favourite spot
So it looks like the tip
Has a permanent dot.

They crowd on my chin
Like they're having a chat
How come I'm so thin
And my spots are so fat?

So I zap them with cream
And yell at them, "DIE!"
But they pay me no heed
And squirt pus in my eye.

I wouldn't mind so much, but my pal, Benny, doesn't have any.

MARGARET RYAN

Fisherman's Tale

By the canal
I was quietly fishing
when a bowler hat
floated by,
stopped level with my eye
and began to rise.

Below it was a man's head
wearing spectacles;
he asked,
"This way to Brackley?"
"Straight ahead."
The face sank back
beneath the wet,

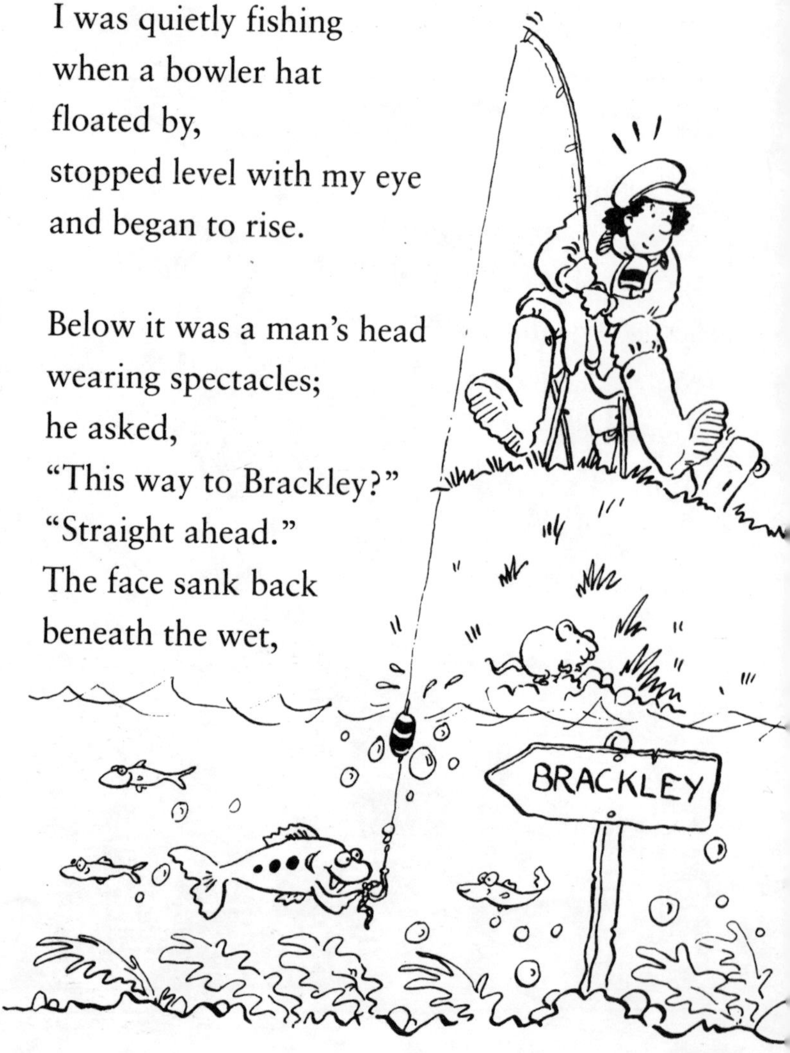

but I was thinking
Brackley's seven miles,
it's getting late;
perhaps he doesn't know
how far.

I tapped the hat
with my rod; again
the face rose; "Yes?"
"You'll need to hurry
to arrive before dark."
"Don't worry," he said,
"I'm on my bike."

IRENE RAWNSLEY

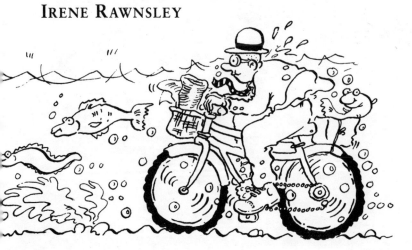

7

Lovely Mosquito

Lovely mosquito, attacking my arm
As quiet and still as a statue,
Stay right where you are! I'll do you
no harm –
I simply desire to pat you.

Just puncture my veins and swallow your fill
For nobody's going to swot you.
Now, lovely mosquito, stay perfectly still –
A SWIPE! and a **SPLAT!** and **I GOT YOU!**

DOUG MACLEOD

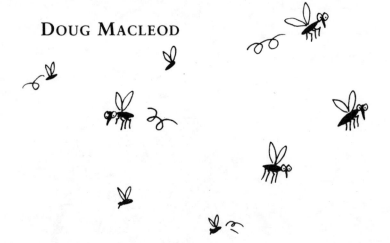

My Cousin Melda

My Cousin Melda
she don't make fun
she ain't afraid of anyone
even mosquitoes
when they bite her
she does bite them back
and say –
"Now tell me, how you like that?"

GRACE NICHOLS

10

Cousin Nell

Cousin Nell
married a frogman
in the hope
that one day
he would turn into
a handsome prince.

Instead he turned into
a sewage pipe
near Gravesend
and was never seen again.

ROGER McGOUGH

The Rave

I'm going with a friend to a sort of ... thing,
Look, I'm just going out, all right?
It's some kind of dreadful, drawn-out do
Where you have to stay the night.
And everybody's going there,
Yes, everyone I know,
So will it be OK then, Mum?
Is it all right if I go?

What's it to do with? ... um ... the church!
No, I don't go as a rule,
It's just a boring little dance
Held by the ... Sunday School.
It's bound to be a real drag,
I said I'd help out, though,
So is it all right, then, Mother? Please,
Is it all right if I go?

13

How do I think I'm getting there?
In a minibus, I think,
Of course there won't be any boys,
No, of course there won't be drink.
Yes, this is a miniskirt,
Well, don't you think it's hot?
It's just a little bit of lipstick, Mum,
Now, can I go or not?

Make sure I'm in by half past EIGHT?
(But it doesn't start till nine!)
My knee-length dress with the lace and bows
Would really *not* look fine!
These? These are only my new shoes,
No, I will not break my neck.
Why don't you trust me!!! What do you mean
You phoned the church to check?

JEANNE WILLIS

15

My Brother Said

My brother said, "I'll flatten you,
I'll tip you off your feet,
I'll push your teeth to the back of your head,
I'll knock you from here to next week.
I'll marmalise you, I'll exterminate you,
I'll change the shape of your face,
when I've finished, you won't even look
as if you belong to the human race!
I'll really give you a hiding,
I'll clobber you, I'll make you wail.
I'm going to make you regret it,
your face will really turn pale.
I'll hammer you, I'll rattle your bones,
I'll fill you full of dread."

And I only told his girlfriend
that he still takes his teddy to bed!

BRIAN MOSES

Decisions

GET your hair cut, says my mum.
It's really in a state.
The ends of it are trailing in
The fried egg on your plate.

DON'T get your hair cut, says my pal.
Leave it. What the heck!
If you get it cut you'll have
To wash your dirty neck.

GET your hair cut, says my dad.
It really is a sight.
A couple of birds could nest in it
Completely out of sight.

DON'T get your hair cut, barks my dog.
Look what they did to me.
Bald as a baby's bottom
Because of one tiny flea.

Do I WANT my hair cut?
Maybe I do ... or don't.
I'll make up my mind tomorrow,
Or maybe again ... I won't.

MARGARET RYAN

The Teacher Says

I was sharpening my pencil, that's all.
"Sit down," said Miss.
"Only one person is allowed
to wander around this room
and it's me."

"But he's got nothing to write with,"
said my mate Kev,
"unless he uses his fingernails!"
"Stop calling out," she said.
"Only one person is allowed
to shout in this classroom
and it's me."

I pretended to use my fingernails.
"Now you're being stupid," she said.
"Only one person is allowed
to be stupid in this classroom
and it's me!"

IRENE RAWNSLEY

Rather Him Than Me

There was an old man of Madrid,
Who ate sixty-five eggs for a quid.
When they asked, "Are you faint?"
He replied, "No I ain't,
But I don't feel as well as I did."

ANON.

Elephants

Elephants
aren't any more important
than insects

but I'm on the side
of elephants

unless one of them tries
to crawl up my leg

JOHN NEWLOVE

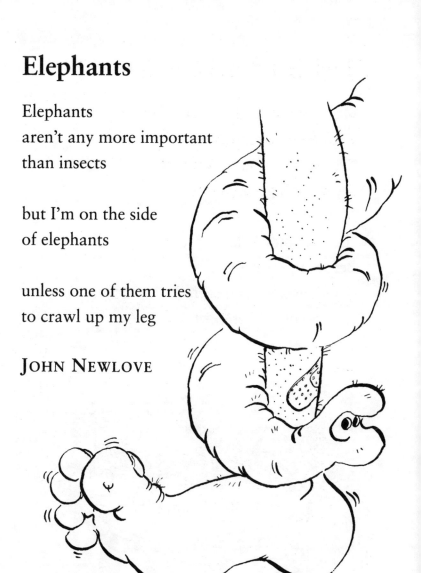

The Glutton

Oh Molly, Molly, Molly
I've eaten too much pie
I've eaten too much custard
I think I'm going to die!

Just one more plate of jelly
Before I pass away
Another glass of lemonade
And then no more I say!

hiccup

Perhaps just one banana
And one more lollipop
A little slice of Eccles cake
And then I'll *have* to stop!

So now one more one more Goodbye!
And one more slice of ham
And now goodbye forever
But first some bread and jam

So now I die, goodbye again
But pass the Stilton cheese
And as I slowly pass away
Just one more dinner please.

SPIKE MILLIGAN

UCKG!

Once I went to the fridge —
saw our jug in there
and I thought:
what's in it?
A syrup
what syrup?
smell it — smells nice
finger in — lick it —
tastes nice
lift the jug and drink a bit
this is good
this is peach syrup
what a drink!
so I drank the lot.

Not long after — a few days later —
I went to the fridge
saw our jug in there
what's in it?
A syrup
what syrup?

smell it
O yes this is the peach syrup again
lift the jug and drink some
drink some more, drink some more
drank the lot.

Not long after — a few days later
I went to the fridge
saw our jug in there
what's in it?
A syrup — yes!
here we go again
lift the jug and fill my mouth
with that thick sweet juice

Uckg!
this isn't peach
this is uckg.
my mouth is full of oil
thick cooking oil

I wonder
who put *that* there?

MICHAEL ROSEN

27

Memories

Do you remember that day?
Do you?
When you walked right into it,
Huge!
Your whole shoe was in it,
SQUISHY!
And there was no grass,
YEUCH!
But it didn't smell,
PHEW!
That ice-cream
on your shoe!

BRETT FITZCHARLES

I'm the Big Sleeper

I'm the Big Sleeper
rolled up in his sheets
at the break of day
I'm a big sleeper living soft
in a hard kind of way
the light through the curtain
can't wake me

I'm under the blankets
you can't shake me
the pillow rustler
and blanket gambler
a mean tough eiderdown man

I keep my head
I stay in bed

MICHAEL ROSEN

Cat Envy

The cat is sleeping on my bed.
She's lucky she can sleep, instead
Of lying worrying all night
And wishing she was black and white
Or wondering why the cat next door
Has stopped being friendly any more.
And no one's going to wake her up
And yell, "Bring down that empty cup,"
Or "If you don't get moving you'll
Be twenty minutes late for school."

Compared with mine, her life is simple.
She never has to squeeze a pimple.
She doesn't try to look eighteen
To see the film her friends have seen.
She sometimes gives herself a groom
But no one makes her clean her room.
She doesn't have to wash her bowl
Before she goes out for a stroll,
And no one stays up late to hiss,
"What time of night do you call this?"

No wonder she can sleep like that.
I sometimes wish I was the cat.

JULIA DONALDSON

Spending

Spending
a
penny
cost
five
pence
in
St. Ives.
So
I
waited
inside
'til I'd
been
five
times

GARY BOSWELL

The Rabbit's Christmas Carol

I'm sick as a parrot,
I've lost me carrot,
I couldn't care less if it's
Christmas Day.

I'm sick as a parrot,
I've lost me carrot,
So get us a lettuce
Or ... go away!

KIT WRIGHT

Bogeyman Headmaster

Our headmaster is a bogeyman
Our headmaster is a bogeyman
and he'll catch you if he can.

He creeps through the window
when the school is closed at night
just to give the caretaker a fright.

Our headmaster is a bogeyman
Our headmaster is a bogeyman
and he'll catch you if he can.

When he walks
his feet never touch the ground.
When he talks
his mouth never makes a sound.
That's why assembly is so much fun.

You should see him float through the air
when we say our morning prayer
and at assembly the teachers get trembly
when the piano starts to play on its own.
It's our bogeyman headmaster having a
bogeyman joke.

Only the lollipop lady doesn't feel scared
cause when he tried his bogeyman trick
she said, "Buzz off or I'll hit you with my
stick!"

Life can be lonely
for our bogeyman headmaster
but from his office you can always hear
this strange sound of laughter.

JOHN AGARD

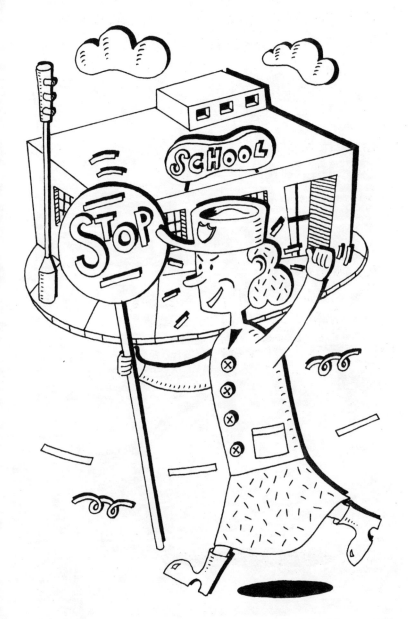

Have You Read...?

Enjoy Your Homework	by R.U. Joking
Out for the Count	by I.C. Stars
Cliff-Top Rescue	by Justin Time
A Year in Space	by Esau Mars
Your Turn to Wash Up	by Y. Mee
Off to the Dentist	by U. First
Broken Windows	by E. Dunnett
Pickpocket Pete	by M. T. Purse
Lions on the Loose	by Luke Out
Helping Gran	by B.A. Dear
Ten Ice-creams	by Segovia Flaw
Rock Concert	by Q. Here

JUDITH NICHOLLS

I Know a Man

I know a man who eats ears.
He cooks them first,
Likes them crisp and salty
To build up his thirst.

I know a man who eats tongues,
So fresh they almost moo.
He licks his lips as he eats,
Tasting his own tongue, too.

I know a man who eats ears
And tongues. I met him down South.
But I kept my balaclava on
And never opened my mouth.

CELIA WARREN

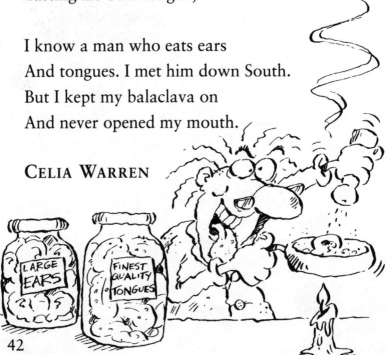

42

There was an old woman

There was an old woman lived in a shoe
spent her entire life
going round
saying
"Poooooh!"

GARY BOSWELL

Third Year Girls

Sarah Best, Sarah Best
Wears a bra and not a vest

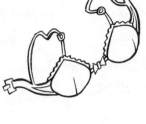

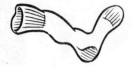

Charlotte Cox, Charlotte Cox
Wears black tights and never socks.

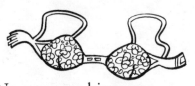

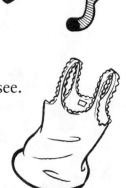

Wendy Ray, Wendy Ray
Kissed a boy the other day.

No one ever kisses me,
I'm still in vests and socks, you see.

Jeanne Willis

44

A Little Nut-Tree

I had a little nut-tree,
Nothing would it bear.
I searched in all its branches,
But not a nut was there.

"Oh, little tree," I begged,
"Give me just a few."
The little tree looked
   down at me
And whispered,
"Nuts to you."

ROALD DAHL

INDEX OF FIRST LINES